A CRAZY FLIGHT
and Other Poems

Myra Cohn Livingston

A CRAZY FLIGHT

AND OTHER POEMS

Illustrated by James J. Spanfeller

HARCOURT, BRACE & WORLD, INC., NEW YORK

To Jennie

Text copyright © 1969 by Myra Cohn Livingston
Illustrations copyright © 1969 by Harcourt, Brace & World, Inc.

First edition
Library of Congress Catalog Card Number: 69–13775
Printed in the United States of America

Contents

When I Can Fly

When I can fly
(with my own wings)
more easily,
I will fasten them on,
open the window,
and step out into the air.
I will sail over the city
and arrive at school
on top of the roof
just when the bell rings.

The way things are now,
I put on my clothes,
run down the stairs,
open the door,
scuffle down the walk
and into the street,
counting cracks, counting blocks,
waiting for traffic lights,
passing all the stores,
and it takes so long.

When I can fly
(with my own wings),
it will be much better.

Be My Circle

Be my circle,
I said to my mother.
Be my circle,
And I will run around you
Today
And every tomorrow.

Be my circle, Mother.

Being Fat

Being fat
    is mostly that
    people talk at
    your stomach.

It's all of you, right there
in the middle of you. No one talks to
your face or eyes or ears.
Just your stomach.

And this big old fat stomach of mine
grows and grows.

Going Away

The world they speak of
Is far away. Over the mountain.
I could walk and walk and never get there.

And now you are going.

The plane will fly you up to clouds
Hanging over the mountain. And I will walk
On sidewalks. And look up to the sky.

I think of you flying.

Coming Home

And when you come home,
My face looks at your face.
It is just what I remember.

It was hard to think of your eyes
When you were gone.
It was hard to hear your voice call me.

Now that I know you again
I sing.

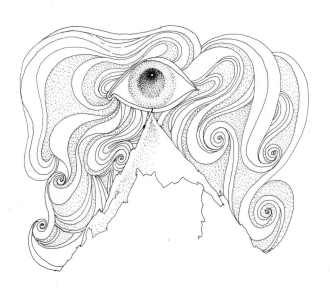

Birds Asleep

I have always imagined
the birds asleep.
No more singing, no quarreling about worms.
They just turn sleepy.
They want to rest.
Birds, with their feathers smooth, their wings
     folded down tight, tucked about them,
     about their heads, closing their eyes.

But where do they sleep?
Where?

City in Summer

On summer nights
    the lights
    go dancing on buildings,
    blue dancing green
    dancing white dancing
    red

    and I can be in bed
    dreaming the lights
    of summer nights
    going dancing.

In Quiet Night

In quiet night
the horns honking up from the street
make mad voices
to other horns, tires screech
to other tires, brakes shriek
to other brakes.

Somewhere, there is a night of trees,
of great, bulging bullfrogs croaking
in ponds. Screech owls cry to a forest
of birds
    shrieking.

Horns, in quiet night, honk up songs
no frog, no bird, has ever sung.

Construction

And every time I pass
The building grows up,
Grows up, window to window,
Stretching taller to the sky.

Diggers come. Big cats come.
Cranes come painted with words.
And every time I pass
The building grows up.

Sky men come with torches.
Sparks fly. Steel beams clank.
And every time I pass
The building grows up taller.

One day, a truck will come
Bringing a sign. Then I will know
Who, with diggers and cats and cranes,
Sparks, torches, and beams,
Grows this building.

The Dead Ones

Scrunch,
I go to the leaves.
Scrunch,
You big heap of brown leaves on the curb.
   (Into pieces scrunching, into scratchy
      paper pieces
   gritting in my shoes, into little
      brittle pieces
   snapping and broken and dead.)

It is hard to remember you
last spring
when you were tender, uncurling, tree-green.
It is hard to remember you
this winter
grown old and hard
and brown
and dead
and only good for scrunching.

Green Park Dream

Once I had a dream.
Not like any other dream at all.
It happened in the park.

The slide was tall,
Taller than the way to space.
I climbed and climbed the steps.
Friends climbed with me,
Strangers stood below.
They all called hello
In this green park dream.

But the part I liked best,
The part I will always remember,
Was sliding down,
     sliding down that slippery sliver of steel—

How Little I Was

How little I was then
To make it happen
When I lifted my feet,
Raised my arms,
Wriggled myself around,
Whispered the magic word,
And there I was

Flying.
Flying!

If the Jay Would Stop

If the jay would stop,
I would paint him
    high
    in our elm,
    with the blue of sky
    no brighter than he,
    the cloud of white not so
    white as his vest,
    his cry so loud
    I can never put in my picture,
       yet

    I hear his cry when the paint
       shines wet.

Real Estate

The pigeons own the building,
That gray one, there.
They're always sitting on it,
Talking. About the weather, I guess,
About what to eat for breakfast
And when to fly off, and where to go
And where to walk and in-between-what-feet
And cooing about the people they see
On the sidewalk
Walking in their round eyes.

O Beautiful Here

O beautiful here, water
Bubbles in clear foam,
Warming to the sun at top,
Shivery to bone :
Floating in cool nothingness
Blue pool waters brim :
O beautiful here, water,
Weightless, I swim.

It Happens Once in a While

Uncle Tiger just went out under the tree
    to get some sun.
He must have been tired. Sometimes,
    he gets that way.
He just stretched out with his long
    yellow paws quiet,
Half shutting his green eyes,
And then along came this silly,
    scolding old jay
And swooped down from the skies.
(You should have heard the riot!)
Uncle Tiger jumping up and biting
    that bright blue jay
And tearing off his feathers,
    one by one,
And, proud as can be,
Brings the jay to me.

It happens, once in a while.

And Once

And once, a stranger smiled at me,
Not knowing my name.
All the same,
Passing by, he smiled at me.

Little People

Little people, thin people, dance on my arm
in the sun; join hands and turn; this way, that
way turn; slowly, so slowly dance and turn again;

yet I have never watched, on other peoples' arms
the little thin, dancing, turning hair-people.

March

The wind is big enough
To move trees
Today.

Palms dance their fronds.
Pines jiggle skinny arms.
Oaks thrash, sycamores fight,
Willows touch low.

The magnolia drops its blossoms
Sadly.

Mrs. Elsinore

Oh, she's mean,
That Mrs. Elsinore.
She shouts and yells when we play ball.
She doesn't like children. Not at all.
That's why we dump garbage at her front door
On Halloween.

Someday

I know the language of the ocean,
A language we speak together often,
A secret language we share.

I listen to the ocean. I hear him.

Boats ruffle my waves, he says.
Divers bubble my deep.
Surfers roll on me.
Fish talk in me.
Gulls tiptoe my foam.

All this he tells me, and more.

Someday I will try to teach you
How the ocean speaks.

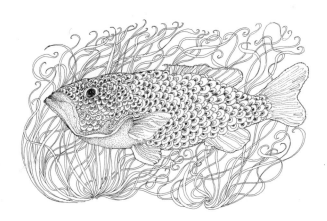

Nobody Gives It to You

Nobody gives it to you.
Nobody says it's exactly yours.
   The blue, the green, the white of it;
   The air stinging your nose, sucking
     your mouth,
   The wind scamping you along the sidewalk,
   The leaves crunching under your feet,
   The fall : The crispy ting of it.
Nobody says it's exactly yours,
Nobody gives it to you.
But it is.

No

No. I never saw a cow.
Not close up so I could see the milk
And hear the moo.

But once, riding in the country
Roads, someone pointed and told me to look.
   "Cows"—they shouted—"cows!
    Cows make milk! Cows give meat!
    Look! They eat the grass."

I looked quick
And I could see it was true.
They were eating the grass.
They were softly eating.
They scarcely moved.

I never saw the milk, close up, or the meat.
I never heard the moo.

Pine

Many arms
and fingers,
long and thin and prickly,
and little heads of brown that
tumble down
all sticky,
and a
sharp
stingy
smell
of fall :
My pine tree stands
alone,
tall.

Rain-Walking

Walk in the
raining
puddles of mud
puddlejump
over a pool
walk in the
raining the raining
of mud
the puddles of raining to
school
slickers wet yellow
red brick boots
plop
in the
puddlejumps
slop
walk in the
raining
of black mirror streets
walk in the
raining
won't
stop

Skinny Jim

Skinny Jim
Climbs up a tree.

"Hey there, Jim,
Whatdaya see?"

        "I see a tree
            As tall and thin
            As ever I have
            Ever been.
            Its skin
            All tanned
            And tight
            Like me.
            Its arms
            And trunk
            And fingers be
            Like me,
            All thin,
            All tight, bone skin.

    "This tree I like,"

    Says Skinny Jim.

The Sun Is Stuck

The sun is stuck.
I mean, it won't move.
I mean it's hot, man, and we need a red-hot
   poker to pry it loose,
Give it a good shove and roll it across
   the sky
And make it go down
So we can be cool,
Man.

This Thing Called Space

It might be just beginning,
This Space,
This vacant place
Beyond Earth.

But if clouds keep rolling
White; if they keep turning gray and black,
Blowing in wind and rain and snowing and
All the Space is hidden,
How will I see it?
How will I know?

Wharf

There's that smell of the boats.
Sometimes you have to hold your nose
To keep it out, that smell;
But when it's keen, when it's stinking,
It gets you to thinking about the fishermen
Off the shore. The lobsters, snappers,
Baby pink shrimp, the albacore,
And how, with nets, the fishermen bob
    their boats
To sea. To sea. To catch the fish.

This Story

This story she told me,
This story came into my head.
It came into my head so bright
That I could think about it later

And wonder on it. Wonder how
This story came into me
As though I knew it always
And would know it forever.

What If

Oh, what if the Easter Bunny
    should shed his pink ears?
    his white fur?
    should leap away?
    never leaving an egg?
    never weaving a basket?
Oh, what if the Easter Bunny
    should turn into a
    March Hare?

The One I Always Get

And I step on the bus
And I put my money in the glass box
And I find a seat in front
        (it's better for jiggling)
And old women don't sit there
        (it's better for watching)
And you don't get squished.

And we speed up going down Wilshire
        (when people aren't waiting at bus stops)
And this driver, the one I always get, shrugs
        (when he's through counting transfers and
        winding up his money box)
And looks at me when he's pulling up at
        La Brea :

"Well," he says, "time for you to get off and
        get to your homework."
"Well," I say, looking back with my left eye
        and swinging around the pole and
        stepping down to the door,
"Well," I say, "see you tomorrow same
        as always."

                "Same as always," he mumbles
And swings the wheel to the curb,
And I jump off.

The Box

I've taken it down
From the high shelf,
The box marked OLD TOYS:
    A silly stuffed chicken with a missing eye,
    A farmhouse painted red with a spotted cow,
    A set of blocks and a ball made of fuzz,
    A puzzle with only five pieces,
    A giraffe with a bent neck.

    Why did I play with those old things, anyway?

In This Jungle

In this jungle
I will search an elephant,
A huge elephant, gray, with pink eyes.

It is quiet now,
But I understand
That if I listen carefully,
If I crouch very still,
If I wait patiently,
He will come.

> Boughs break.
> Feet thunder.
> Branches fly.
> And there will be a world of trumpeting

When he comes.
When my elephant comes.

Why?

I don't know why I'm so crazy.
It just happens some days.
The air full of laughing
And dancing and spinning around
And sillies and giggling
And there I am. Crazy with it.

So I spin
And I dance
And I laugh
And I giggle

And all of it whirls up together
Inside me and has to come spilling out

Crazy.

November

Trees worry in November.
They worry and grow old.
They turn their leaves gold and red and brown,
Wither,
Drop them down.

Then they stand,
Naked, cold.
They worry a lot.
They look
Afraid.

Tehachapi Mountains

They are sleeping, these velvet elephants,
Sleeping in Tehachapi. Sleeping so deeply
That in their dreams they dream they are
Mountains.

The Wind of Spring

The wind has picked me up,
Picked me up and out from all the others.
He is blowing me away from April
    Into May.

Wind, who blows the poppy's face to pieces,
Wind, who sweeps the Scotch broom in the air,
Wind, who pulls the juniper's long fingers—
    Blow me out from April
    Into May.

Tomorrow

It lives there
In one small corner of my head,
    Sailing sky to moon's ocean,
    Swimming green to ocean's deep,
    Dreaming new hours, new times.
    It bubbles, bursts a new explosion :

It is the growing up,
The tomorrow
Of me.

A Crazy Flight

The world is lazy turning
When you wait.
The sun, a silly tortoise, crawls
    across today.
The moon pokes through an endless ride of sky.
But then, for one quick happy day,
A birthday day, they spin and fly.
It's hard to wait.

All earth things change.
Brown trees turn green
And somewhere I have seen
A rocket out of range,

Your rocket, flying past the moon
And into sun. And with a satellite
And you, in space,
I wish you, child, a crazy flight.

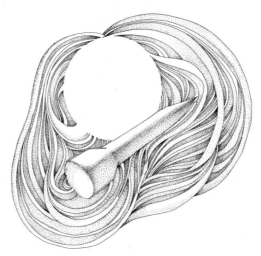